MW00626895

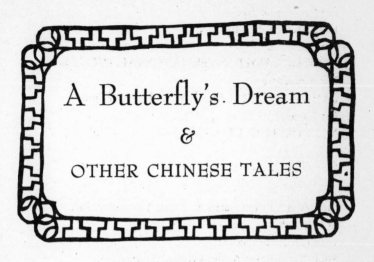

A Butterfly's Dream

&

OTHER CHINESE TALES

retold by Cheou-Kang Sié

**Former Ambassador to the Holy See
from the Republic of China
Full Member, Belgian Royal Academy
of French Literature**

paintings by Chi Kang

CHARLES E. TUTTLE COMPANY

Rutland, Vermont & Tokyo, Japan

REPRESENTATIVES
For Continental Europe:
BOXERBOOKS, INC., *Zurich*
For the British Isles:
PRENTICE-HALL INTERNATIONAL, INC., *London*
For Australasia:
PAUL FLESCH & CO., PTY. LTD., *Melbourne*
For Canada:
M. G. HURTIG, LTD., *Edmonton*

Published by the Charles E. Tuttle Company, Inc.
of Rutland, Vermont & Tokyo, Japan
with editorial offices at
Suido 1-chome, 2-6, Bunkyo-ku, Tokyo

Copyright in Japan, 1970
by Charles E. Tuttle Co., Inc.

Library of Congress Catalog Card No. 70-125561
International Standard Book No. 0-8048-0077-4

First printing, 1970

Line drawings by S. Katakura
PRINTED IN JAPAN

TO HIS HOLINESS POPE PAUL VI
Gloriously Reigning
with most respectful and
humble homage
of greatest admiration and deepest gratitude

Other works by the same author:

Table of Contents

Preface

An unexpected effect of World War II, with its blackouts, *ausweis,* and manhunts, was that I, along with many others, who would have been occupied in other ways, found time to read and to learn those things we ordinarily put off for more propitious times.

When the war came, I was at my post representing my country at the Holy See, which was sealed off from Italy and the rest of the world. Owing to this exceptional situation, I had much enforced leisure, which I used to learn English, since French was my only Western language.

After a few months of study, in order to become more intimately acquainted with English, I started to write these twelve traditional Chinese tales and legends. Marooned as I was in the 110 acres of Vatican City, without sources of reference, I was forced to rely upon my memory for facts and dates. What I have attributed to the poet Tsien Kee Yeh, for instance, might well have happened to the poet Chao Song Si. In fact, once the point of departure was found, my imagination wandered along the way and the outcome evolved according to my fancy.

Oddly enough, although these stories were first written 9

in English, they were first published in French. This is how that came about. While I was taking part in the Peace Conference in Luxembourg Palace, I was also participating in the first conference for the organization of the United Nations Educational, Scientific and Cultural Organization. There I was often asked for some of my literary works for publication. My laziness led me to translate these, my first creative writing in English, into French to fulfill my commitment.

The origins of these tales are varied. *A Butterfly's Dream, Old Man Stupidity, The Return,* and *Spring Water* come from the philosophical writings of Twang-Tze and Lie-Tze (400 B.C.). *The Clay Statues* and *Vinegar* were taken from famous memoirs of the 17th century. Popular legends provided the themes of *The Bridge of Magpies, Fetal Education,* and *Gratitude. The Reward* and *Illusion* were inspired by the 17th-century *Extraordinary Stories* of Liau Tsai, while the love drama of *Tso Ying Tie* was mentioned in the civil records of the Kwei Kee District in Chekiang Province.

Some of the stories have appeared in the French language in reviews, such as *Sinologica,* published in Basel, Switzerland; and in *Les Nouvelles Litteraires,* Paris. They had the good fortune to be well received. Now I venture to present them in my original English text.

I hope that these stories prove worthy of their source in Chinese culture. If I have done as we Chinese phrase it, "wasted raw materials," I apologize to our ancestors, who have left behind so many priceless treasures.

Cheou-Kang Sié

A Butterfly's Dream

A Butterfly's Dream

 Twang Tsen, the well-known Taoist philosopher, related a dream of his as follows:

He dreamt that he was a butterfly. At the beginning he felt somewhat awkward, since it was the first time he had been such a creature. Soon other butterflies gave him a friendly welcome and one after the other said:

Why do you stay in a corner like a little girl?
The gods created nature for us.
And the sweetness of flowers, too.
Love is delicious.
The sun calls us.
Come with us.

With such words in his ears, he behaved then as befitted his appearance and, bit by bit, really became a butterfly. He flitted alone or with others from flower to flower. He quenched his thirst with the dew from the rose. He challenged the variegated chameleons with his multicolored body; and the perfume of the lily, the jasmine, and the honeysuckle inebriated him.

When he remembered he was a male, he courted female butterflies, who not only allowed themselves to be charmed but delighted in his fascination, some even provoking him.

All the butterflies seemed to live from minute to minute. Unlike animals and still less like human beings, the butterflies did not appear to him to have a warlike nature, worries of life, fears of death, and complicated feelings such as jealousy.

So it happened that one male butterfly told him joyfully:

"Come, I'll show you an adorable female to whom I have just made love. I think she may have 70, 68, 84, and comma 98!"

"What on earth do you mean by those figures?"

"That's a convention of ours. The first number means the percentage for looks, the second for colors, the third for perfume, and after the comma for sex appeal."

"Then show her to me at once. She must surely be a dream."

In truth, this marvel was charm itself. Attracted, he began to make love to her, while his friend and the others flew round the couple very pleased. The happiness of the two was so great and wild that he woke up.

Himself once more, he was bitterly tormented. Butterfly life was so carefree, and human life . . .

Finally, after reflection, he said to himself: There is nothing to worry about. Who knows, maybe *my* life is only a *butterfly's* dream.

13

But the image of her never left his mind. While he dreamt about her that afternoon, the bookboy—a youth whose task was to attend to the master and look after the books—brought in his cup of tea with a letter.

Roused, he sipped his tea and read the letter. The more he read, the more his excitement grew. He had had many letters from her, but none of them was so sincere. so deeply felt, so moving. Joyfully he held up the letter to the bookboy; he wanted somebody to share his joy—so great it was.

"That's from a lady, from a young, beautiful, intelligent lady. She'll come and stay with us."

With that, he went to the lady. Her first words were:

"So you are willing to accept me as your servant, as your slave. . . ."

"No, no, as my wife, as my queen. . . ."

Then, for the first time, they kissed, and their union was decided. He wandered about on his way home, young, light, and smiling.

Although the honeymoon was not a Chinese custom, they traveled. By day, as poets do, they "wandered around mountains and delighted in water." In the evening they amused themselves writing poetry. Sometimes one would compose a poem and the other, using the same rhymes, would compose another; sometimes they would write a poem together, alternately contributing the verses; sometimes again, they would form poems by "gathering verses" from known poets. Love was always the subject, naturally.

After the honeymoon, they came home. He took her around the gardens. She was amazed at their magnificence.

The Clay Statues

It was afternoon, a fine, sunny, showery day of late April. A famous poet, Tsieng Kee Yeh, sat in his library with a book he was unable to continue reading.

Still very handsome, he bore his sixty years lightly. His fine regular features, which, according to his acquaintances, had been oversharp before, had softened with age. Were it not for his white hair, one might have thought him a young man sitting there.

He was actually somewhat pensive, somewhat intoxicated by the perfume of the blossom, wafted through the open windows by the breeze. Soon he entered into a state between slumber and dream.

A little more than a year ago he had lost his adorable wife. The beauty of the springtime recalled her vividly to him and also made him think perplexedly and more acutely of another woman, Weeping Willow. Weeping Willow, the very name he had given her. . . . He pondered vaguely on the fleetingness of earthly things.

Weeping Willow was a very fashionable courtesan whom
he had known some months before. Barely twenty, she

dazzled all with the beauty of her classic profile, autumnal water eyes, lotus-bud mouth, and the glamour of her peach complexion. Slim, fragile, and lissome like her name, she had "a stock of sadness and a tendency to illness," which made her highstrung, emotional, and hypersensitive. All this helped her to compose charming lyric poetry. Moreover, her classical calligraphy showed much character, elegance, and refinement. She might have come of a very good family.

It was natural that such a creature should attract the poet. The first time they met they immediately treated each other as old friends. After that he often went to see her. Before a burning incense jar, they would drink tea, speak of literature, and speculate on trifling things. Sometimes she would play old airs on the lute of seven strings. Then a nameless melancholy would seize them both.

A fortnight earlier she had shyly shown him a poem of hers, in which she alluded to the legendary "one-in-two fish"—a one-eyed fish that by itself could see on one side only and, to have complete vision, had to have a partner. At that he was extremely happy. They parted with few words but were quite moved.

He paced to and fro much of the night. How could he accept this sacrifice? He who was so "near the woods." Could she find happiness with him? Would she regret her decision afterward? He turned the question over and over in his mind.

Happy, though anxious and tormented, he remained undecided. He had not since dared to go to her.

But the image of her never left his mind. While he dreamt about her that afternoon, the bookboy—a youth whose task was to attend to the master and look after the books—brought in his cup of tea with a letter.

Roused, he sipped his tea and read the letter. The more he read, the more his excitement grew. He had had many letters from her, but none of them was so sincere. so deeply felt, so moving. Joyfully he held up the letter to the bookboy; he wanted somebody to share his joy—so great it was.

"That's from a lady, from a young, beautiful, intelligent lady. She'll come and stay with us."

With that, he went to the lady. Her first words were:

"So you are willing to accept me as your servant, as your slave. . . ."

"No, no, as my wife, as my queen. . . ."

Then, for the first time, they kissed, and their union was decided. He wandered about on his way home, young, light, and smiling.

Although the honeymoon was not a Chinese custom, they traveled. By day, as poets do, they "wandered around mountains and delighted in water." In the evening they amused themselves writing poetry. Sometimes one would compose a poem and the other, using the same rhymes, would compose another; sometimes they would write a poem together, alternately contributing the verses; sometimes again, they would form poems by "gathering verses" from known poets. Love was always the subject, naturally.

After the honeymoon, they came home. He took her around the gardens. She was amazed at their magnificence.

They stretched for miles. Adjoining the house was a velvety lawn with trees on either side which led to a trellised avenue where wisteria, rambler roses, honeysuckle, and jasmine perfumed the air. On the left of the avenue was a grass plot with flower beds and a row of goldfish tanks. Behind these were rock gardens, camellia trees, and hothouses. On the right of the avenue, twin lakes were connected by a hump-backed bridge, on the top of which was a temple with two clay statues: the God and Goddess of the Earth. The larger lake was bordered by weeping willows, and the smaller covered with water lilies, which, since they are considered to be "gentleman flowers," gave the smaller lake the nickname of Gentleman Lake. Though growing in the dirty mud, their roots keep their extreme whiteness, hence the nickname. Beyond Gentleman Lake at the top of a hill stood a pavilion that had two floors, on the lower floor a lounge and two rooms, with a large reception room above them.

When Weeping Willow, led by the poet, walked in the gardens, the flowers seemed to bid her welcome, the irises, buttercups, narcissuses, bluebells, and wood anemones which tinged the brushwood everywhere. They passed most of their time in the gardens or in the pavilion. She especially liked going to the small temple on the bridge to admire the extensive view and to contemplate the two clay statues, having under her feet the "gentleman flowers."

It happened that the statues were broken in a spring storm and became a shapeless mass. When the lovers saw this, they were much upset. Before this desolation they remained 19

silent a long time and at length the same idea crossed both their minds. They then took turns improvising a poem. The poet began:

> We loved each other passionately,
> But we were divided by our bodies.

Weeping Willow took it up:

> A blessed storm united us completely,
> With all the flowers as witnesses.
> If, one day, an artist should remold this same clay,
> And make again two statues,
> Then there would be you in me,
> And there would be me in you.

★　　★　　★

The happy days passed quickly, and the Feast of Chrysanthemums came with autumn. There was a Chrysanthemum Day in the poet's gardens. These flowers have always been much appreciated by poets. Known as "hermit flowers," they bear the frost lightly and bloom beautifully but very late, as if they disdain to compete with the other flowers. About two thousand potted chrysanthemums, of more than a thousand varieties, were on show. In the morning the public was admitted. In the afternoon, with Weeping Willow, the poet gave a reception in honor of their friends. When all had admired the flowers, the poet and Weeping Willow led their guests to the pavilion where a "crab-wine" party was given.

At such a party it was the custom to hold a contest to find the most skillful in decorating crabs. Weeping Willow was the winner. When she had taken out all the flesh from a crab, she succeeded in fitting its shell together again. After this competition, they washed their fingers with chrysanthemum leaves in hot water. Then each had a bowl of ginger and cane-sugar soup. Finally, they drank yellow wine and ate "the rice of Night Treasures."

The poet, very joyful, toasted his guests. But, whether overwhelmed by his extreme happiness, whether exhausted by his late nights during these last months, or whether from both these causes, he suddenly fainted. Weeping Willow installed him in the pavilion. From this time forth they lived even more for each other—if that were possible.

Little by little he recovered, thanks to the loving care of Weeping Willow. They were so alone and therefore so happy in the pavilion that they returned no more to the house, even on the approach of winter.

During the winter the lovers enjoyed the snow—played with it and wrote poems about it. One afternoon in the twilight it snowed heavily; they were contemplating the fairylike world, sipping now and then the warmed yellow wine. To enhance the poetry of the moment, she sang his favorite poems, accompanying herself on the lute of seven strings. Exalted, he recited what he was improvising: a poem of alternating regular and blank verse:

Weeping Willow, it's true that the snow flakes
Are very beautiful. The clouds that look like reddish
Steam spread and gather on all sides.

23

Great snow flakes whirl in the air;

The north wind blows violently;

Vision loses itself in the silver horizon.

What man would at such a moment meditate with
    calmness

In his saddle like Meng Ho Ying?

We are now at the season when the cold begins.

Because of that, you say winter has come.

Well, I say it is spring.

If it were not so,

How could the pear blossoms fall petal by petal?

How could the willow-down whirl through the air?

Behold, the pear blossoms mass and make a silvered
    ground;

The willow-down rises to heaven and falls again to
    earth.

Smell—the perfume of the corchorus embalms the air.

I have before my eyes a delightful view;

I am at the happiest moment of my life.

They hold out silken embroidered draperies before me;

They scatter a rich carpet of flowers at my feet;

They serve me rare dishes in golden plates;

They fill silver jars with exquisite wine.

Does my happiness come from all this?

No. Really, I think all this is empty;

My happiness comes from Weeping Willow, my
    goddess.

Because there is me in her,

24 And there is her in me;

And there is us in nature,
And there is nature in us.

★   ★   ★

Alas, it was the swan song of Tsieng Kee Yeh. He died that very night, loving Weeping Willow.

At first she became mad. Then an idea made her calm. She began to dress the poet and lay him out. She dressed herself, went out, and then came back with her arms full of corchorus flowers. She strewed them over the coverlet on the death bed. She left a note on the table. It ran:

He is dead, because he loved me too much;

I am going to him, for I need his love.

Old Man Stupidity

Once an old man, aged ninety years, known as Old Man Stupidity, was digging at the foot of one of the two mountains in front of his house, while his offspring took the removed earth faraway by means of hand-carts, pails, and baskets. They were working heartily and joyfully, though hard.

Another old man, a friend of his of the same age, who was known as Old Man Intelligence, walked by chance to the place he was working. He inquired:

"Hey! Old man, what are you busy at?"

Old Man Stupidity, on seeing his friend, paused a while and then bowed very courteously, as stupidity should to intelligence. Then he replied:

"As you see, I'm moving earth."

"What for?"

"These two mountains hide the view from my house, and when I have to go somewhere, they make the passage difficult. I intend to put them farther away."

"Ha, ha. You move mountains? Let me tell you that moving mountains is beyond human power."

"Yes, I dare say; but all the same, they must go."

"A man of your age should be wiser."

"It has nothing to do with age. I must do the task I have assigned myself."

"Do you imagine you can be successful?"

"I imagine nothing. Imagination kills faith. I am sure there'll be a conclusion."

"Why so?"

"I devote myself entirely to it. When I have passed on, my sons will continue it, and their sons will continue in their turn and so on. As the mountains don't grow and my descendants continue on without one day's rest, surely the task will be completed."

Old Man Intelligence hid his laughter and politely wished success to his friend, but thought delightedly to himself that the stupid man really deserved his title.

The latter went on with his stupidity, naturally.

Later on, an angel flew over the country and saw the work which, though useless, amazed and amused him a great deal. He related the story to the Emperor of Heaven who, touched by such stupidity and faith, ordered two angels to take away the two undesired mountains in one night.

When Old Man Intelligence came again to make fun of his friend and saw no mountains there, he could hardly believe his eyes.

The Bridge of Magpies

On the east bank of the Heavenly River, which is called the Milky Way in Europe, dwelt the celestial Spinning Girl, and on the west bank was the celestial Shepherd Boy. Though very lonely, they both worked hard; so Heaven thrived.

The Emperor of Heaven, having pity on them and wanting to reward their industry, united them as husband and wife. They found in it a happiness they had not imagined. They took such delight in their union that, even after their honeymoon, they were loath to return to work. For months and months they lived with folded arms—which is to say their life was leisurely. But it would be wrong to say that their arms were folded. They spoke of love to each other, they caressed each other, and most of the time they made love to each other.

Soon the consequences of their enviable love were felt: provisions began to run short among the celestial beings. So much so that textiles, meat, milk, and their derivative products were rationed in Heaven. And everyone was very worried over clothes, shoes, and linen. Most goddesses went without stockings and wore wooden-soled shoes, and many were undernourished.

Since they were clever, they had recourse to the black market, which enabled the rich to live well. But the ones with fixed incomes were extremely miserable. Anyhow, all were more or less upset; everybody spoke of and worried over nothing but food and clothes. In the gardens of the rich, as well as in convent gardens, it was not a rare thing to find a milk cow. Even in the imperial gardens, there were about thirty cows in stalls under the Imperial Sculpture Gallery. This mixture of art and rusticity originated from the necessity of sustaining their majesties and the aged high dignitaries. Such a mixture was found also farther on: in a basement behind the Imperial Picture Gallery a dairy was improvised. So art lovers coming from the gallery, with their minds full of artistic visions, were suffocated by a strong and strange odor that might have been a blend of the smell of ripe cheese and the perfume of flowers.

And this general economic crisis caused many a row in the family. The Empress of Heaven herself made a scene with the Emperor about the rationing. Here is what happened. One evening the Emperor waited for his wife a long time to come to dinner. He was impatient, worried, and irritable. At last she arrived. As she appeared to be angry, he immediately became calm, and inquired:

"Darling, has the day gone well?"

"Nowadays nothing's well."

"Oh?"

"Imagine, to manage this household, I—the Empress— 31

have to go to the black market and expose myself to the insolence of those black dealers!"

"Who dared insult you?"

"The one who has a stock of oil."

"How did it happen?"

"He asked one thousand seven hundred illusions (celestial coins) for a flask of oil. I wanted to give him one thousand five hundred. Then this uncouth fellow said, 'Take it or leave it, old girl.' Yes, he actually said that!"

"Don't get so upset; better times will come again. Let's go into dinner."

"I'll not. I've no appetite."

"Come, darling, I promise you it won't happen again."

"Let me alone."

"I'll even stop the rationing. There, are you satisfied?"

"You must do it, you who seem so almighty to us."

He immediately issued an order to separate forever the lazy lovers who were the cause of all the trouble. The decree ran thus:

> Before duty love is nothing, for in order to maintain public order and social organization the notion of duty must be sacred and that of love something secondary. According to our information, the Spinning Girl and the Shepherd Boy have neglected their duty because of love. They are condemned to be separated forever and to be reinstalled in their respective homes to work as in the past. Furthermore, to prevent them from meeting in secret, all the bridges connecting the banks of the Heavenly River are to be destroyed.

Fortunately, the Empress was charitable and wished, as all good sovereigns, to appear very kind to her subjects. She therefore went, unknown to the Emperor, to visit the condemned lovers, who had already been separated several months.

She found the Spinning Girl fading in her lovesickness; she was spinning drearily, despairingly, almost automatically, singing melancholy songs. When the Empress saw the Shepherd Boy, he was weeping before his cows and sheep and goats, which, motionless, hopeless, and apathetic, seemed to take part in their guardian's grief. Touched and somewhat remorseful, the Empress thought to herself: I must lessen the lovers' pain.

That very night, after having displayed "clouds and rain" with the Emperor, she took the opportunity to maneuver with her consummate coyness while he was smoking a cigarette. She began:

"By the way . . . you know . . ."

"What?"

"I don't know if I should tell you."

"Oh, darling, tell me everything."

"This Spinning Girl and this Shepherd Boy . . ."

"What about them?"

"I saw them."

"Well?"

"Well, they are very miserable."

"They deserve to be."

"Y-e-s. But . . . all the same . . . you'd better lighten their suffering."

35

"Why?"

"You know . . . my little one . . . they have their . . . senses just like us."

"Perhaps you're right."

"Of course, I am right. My little pet . . ."

"What?"

"You'll make me very happy if you do something for them."

"You're so interested in the Spinning Girl and the Shepherd Boy?"

"Y-e-s, very much."

"Well, for your sake I'll permit them to meet one night every year."

"Oh, you're too sweet. The boy seems to be so charming, so woeful, and the girl so attractive, so amiable, and, above all, so skillful. You know, it is she who weaves the cloth of the sky, which is known for its seamlessness and proverbially symbolizes the perfect thing."

"You are a seamless-sky-cloth woman."

"Naughty! Don't joke."

"I spoke the truth."

"Really? So they can meet tomorrow?"

"Very well."

"That'll be very fitting. You know, the number seven means skill; tomorrow is the seventh day of the seventh moon. The Spinning Girl will meet her lover again just on that day which bears two figures of skill. Perhaps Fate has willed her to be the symbol of skill. What do you think if we carry out the will of Fate?"

"Could I refuse your skillfulness anything?"
"Silly boy!"

★　★　★

So the Spinning Girl and the Shepherd Boy were to meet the next night. But a difficulty arose: all the bridges had been destroyed as ordered. Happily, the magpies, though chattering all the time, were altruistic and kindly offered to form a bridge for the lovers by keeping close together between the banks of the Heavenly River.

Since that time, the celestial lovers meet every year in the evening of the seventh day of the seventh moon. On that night young girls gaze up at the Heavenly River with the wish in their hearts that the Spinning Girl may endow them with skill. And since that day they have always shown much affection toward magpies because of their generosity to the celestial lovers. The name "Birds of Joy," which they have given to those birds, is indeed very nice.

Vinegar

Once upon a time there was a Chancellor of the Empire who suffered greatly from the absence of offspring. He was an orthodox Confucianist (all Chancellors were), and one of the cornerstones of Confucian doctrine lies in filial piety. Textually, "One of the three omissions of filial piety is to have no descendants." Therefore, with his painful situation, he deemed himself unworthy of Confucius. People generally, having reached a certain age, feel the emptiness of life more acutely if they are not surrounded by children or grandchildren. So, almost an old man, the Chancellor found life without great interest, though he was most comfortable from the material point of view.

His only remedy was to take a concubine (polygamy was still legal) who might give him descendants. The Chancellor had indeed thought of it, but there was an insurmountable difficulty. His wife, who hid under her correct and sweet manners a great firmness and whom he respected much, would not hear of his having a second wife. He then tried to console himself a little—if ever he was consolable—by saying that "it was written."

Meanwhile, a Taoist physician arrived at the capital. He was said to be able to cure all ailments, physical and mental. With injections, herbs, massage, and burnings, he did indeed cure many grave, if not "incurable," illnesses; such cases as stuttering, baldness, flat feet, loss of memory, megalomania, and hallucinations.

In the Imperial Town people spoke of nothing but this famous doctor. When the Chancellor heard this, he gave him a private audience. Very honored, the so-called physician presented himself with pride. The statesman received him with kindly condescension. After the usual words of welcome, he came straight to the point:

"Doctor, I am told that you cure all ills."

"I am at the service of Your Greatness."

"I have a case . . . rather . . . intimate . . ."

As the Chancellor said this with a slight blush, the Taoist thought he understood the hint and replied at once:

"I understand. At your age and with sweet and too exacting concubines, it is necessary . . ."

"No . . ."

"I beg you. I have a lot of tonics of intmediate and lasting effect. Your Greatness will be satisfied."

He was completely wrong, so the Chancellor quickly resumed:

"No, no. I don't mean that!"

"What then, pray?"

"My wife . . ."

"I have also specialities for women."

"It is a very peculiar case."

"I guarantee to cure all cases. Entrust me that of your wife, please."

"Even if it does not concern anything physical?"

"Of course."

"Well, it's about my wife's jealousy."

"Ah!"

A little taken aback, he paused. But before the Chancellor he could not retreat before any malady. He then asked the Chancellor:

"Otherwise she is quite well?"

"Perfectly well."

"Then, permit me to suggest this prescription: eat a boiled pear with cane sugar each evening after dinner."

"That's all?"

"That's all."

"And for how long?"

"I don't know exactly."

"Till the ailment is gone away?"

"Nay, till the patient is gone forever."

"Oh!"

*　　*　　*

Since then the Chancellor was more grieved than ever. So much so that the Emperor perceived his great officer's sorrow.

One day at the end of an audience, he asked the cause. The Chancellor reported all to His Majesty, without omitting the scene with the famous Taoist.

42

Desiring to do something for his devoted Chancellor, the Emperor said decidedly:

"You know I have the power to 'grant death.' "

"Yes, Majesty. But, please, do nothing of that sort. Apart from her jealousy, my wife is perfect."

"Wait a bit. . . . Well, tell her to come and see me tomorrow morning. I'll give her an audience and arrange all this."

"What a great favor! May Your Majesty be successful!"

The happy man went home with the comforting idea that with the intercession of the Emperor he could at last have a concubine and, who knows, with her children, also.

At the beginning of the audience, the Son of Heaven tried to persuade the reluctant wife to be more liberal. Lost efforts. She consented to do everything but this. At length, he said earnestly:

"I am sorry, Madam, but I have to make my Chancellor happy. Listen to this. You must either choose a concubine for your husband or you must drink this cup of poison. I give you two days to think it over."

"If that is the case, I prefer to settle it at once."

So saying, she took the cup without hesitation and swallowed its contents in one draught, while the Emperor delighted at her decidedness. He concluded:

"Fortunately it was only vinegar. You can go home quietly. And tell your husband from me that he may not have a concubine at all."

Since this legendary audience, vinegar has been considered a symbol of jealousy and has entered as such into popular speech. When you say to any Chinese that a person "drinks vinegar," he understands immediately that you mean this person is jealous. And the waiters in Peking restaurants never utter the word "vinegar." Instead of the awful word, they say "shocking," so as not to offend the feelings of anybody.

The Return

A man long exiled from his native land was preparing for his return. A friend came to bid him farewell. Moved, they talked late into the night.

Having tried to console each other on their parting, they began to speak of the journey when the friend said:

"I have never seen your country. Is it a beautiful land? Is the journey pleasant?"

The exile became thoughtful and replied with a sigh:

"Oh, my land is so beautiful. Though it is many a year since I left, still it calls me. And each stage of the journey, coach, boat, and chair, is engraved in my mind."

"Tell me about it, pray"

"From here to the principal town of my country, I take the coach. In the coach, I am sure I shall be overwhelmed to hear the peculiar though dearly familiar accent of my fellow travelers. On reaching a certain town, I must find a boat for the second stage. The boat is now propelled, now towed, now sailed. During much of the time, the boatmen sing songs of homesickness that are most melancholy in the twilight between yellowish sky and blue water. I'm sure it

45

will be hard for me to keep back the tears. . . . Before arriving at my native town, I'll perceive from afar the pointed
roof of the Pavilion of Eight Views rising above the town
wall and situated at the spot where two rivers meet. What
memories this beloved and picturesque pavilion recalls!
How many happy hours have I passed there! The sight of it
alone will thrill me. . . . Soon I'll pass along side the pavilion
and follow the town wall to reach the North Gate. Just in
front of it is a tiny harbor with steps leading to the street. It
was there that my father said goodbye to me when I left. . . .
Could I have imagined that it was to be forever? . . . How
great will be my pain on seeing this harbor again."

To soften his grief, the visitor put in:

"Don't be so sad. . . . Is it far from this harbor to your
house?"

"A fair distance, because our house is outside the town."

"Will you stay in the town for some time or go straight
on?"

"I'll go to see my fifth aunt, no doubt, with those who
come to meet me at the North Gate. Dear Aunt, she taught
me the alphabet when I was a small child. Please God she be
in good health."

"She'll be overjoyed on your return."

"Oh, yes, she'll be very moved, she who was so senti-
mental."

"You'll remain with her a little?"

"We'll take some refreshment at her house, to be sure, and
then the chairs will be waiting to bring me to my home. We
46 leave by the South Gate. Two miles or so farther on, we

come to a river. There we have tea in a teahouse nearby; one always has to wait for the ferryboat. The woman who ran the teahouse was a kind, good-natured soul. With a smile she used to say: 'The water comes from heaven and I have a stock of tea leaves. Take as much tea as you want.' It will be so comforting to hear again this homely woman. After the halt the chair-bearers have a hard walk, for the way undulates with hills and valleys. At the top of the last hill we climb, the trees of our garden appear. Oh, blessed garden where my mother waved to me for the last time. . . ."

So saying, he began to weep like a child. The friend let his emotion spend itself. A long pause . . . then they murmured good night.

The next morning he finished his packing, always in the state of mind of one who has just lost or won something.

In the coach he waited for the emotion on hearing the familiar accent of his fellow travelers. The boatmen sang melancholy songs, indeed, but he was not touched. And even the sight of the Pavilion of Eight Views did not move him at all.

He was amazed to feel no emotion, though he was always expecting it. Just as he was arriving at the famous harbor, he thought to himself: "Now, certainly, it will come at last." But no, it did not come.

The fifth aunt wept to see him while he remained serene. And he found no special comfort in the usual words of the old woman of the teahouse. When he saw the trees in his garden and still felt nothing, he made up his mind not to wait any longer for the emotions that should have been.   47

Spring Water

During the reign of the legendary Emperor Yao, about the 24th century B.C., the whole nation thrived. To reward his virtue and endeavor, Heaven made the wind harmonious and the rain opportune. All his subjects were quietly happy. It goes without saying that there was no crime, no injustice, and no theft. If something, whatever its value, was lost on a public road, nobody would touch it, except to move it to a safe place. The Empress herself contributed to this general prosperity by setting a good example. She devoted her mornings to silkworm cultivation and her afternoons to cotton and linen spinning.

The sole worry of the Emperor was that of discovering a successor. At that time the succession was not yet hereditary but might be given to the wisest man of the Empire. As he felt himself getting older and older, his anxiety became more and more acute. Fortunately there were two men, Shu-yu and Shwang, whose fame was spread far and wide, that of the former even more than that of the latter.

Happy for the existence of these two, the Emperor first went to sound out Shu-yu. On the way he saw for himself that each subject was content in his place and at his work. Shortly before arriving at his destination, he heard some peasants singing the oldest rhymed piece of Chinese literature, accompanying themselves on clay instruments:

> I get up at sunrise.
> I go to sleep at sundown.
> I have dug a pond to have water to drink.
> I have sown a field to have rice to eat.
> The authority of the Emperor has nothing
>   to do with me.

The Emperor said then to himself: They are happy, indeed. I think I am really worthy of Heaven's confidence. May It now grant that Shu-yu accept Its Mandate.

But Shu-yu did not. When the Emperor arrived at his house, a little boy led him to a sort of rudimentary kiosk in the garden where Shu-yu was meditating. He received the visitor with his usual courtesy:

"Welcome, venerable old man."

"I apologize for disturbing you. May I ask if you are Shu-yu himself?"

"That's my humble name."

"Your gracious name sounds in my ears like thunder."

"It's too kind of you to say so. But pray, venerable old man, sit down. I beg to offer you some tea. You must be thirsty after your walk."

"With great pleasure, if it does not trouble you too much."

"Pray, there is no trouble at all. And as I have time and 51

presume you do too, we can, if you like, enjoy nature together, can't we?"

"Oh, yes, by all means. This corner of the country is
beautiful, indeed."

"Farther on, southward, on the hill, the landscape is even
more picturesque, especially about the spring which the
little river comes from."

Then they began to speak of the beauty of mountains and
water, of the carefree life of the birds and their songs, of
the radiance and significance of stars, of the seasonable prosperity of trees and flowers. Music also was the subject of long
consideration. Their taste was in such union and their mutual admiration was so spontaneous that they became friends.

At length, the Emperor decided to come to the main object of his visit. He gradually approached the subject:

"All this greatly rests our hearts. Yet, don't you think that
we must also consider public affairs sometimes?"

Very astonished at this, Shu-yu decidedly replied:

"No, no, public affairs are for the officials and have
nothing to do with us."

"Precisely the ones who are wise, learned, and therefore
suitable ought to be chosen as officials, with the wisest at
their head. So public affairs can go on well and the people be
happy."

"Public affairs! Public affairs! What on earth incites you
to be worried about them? And to mention them to me?"

"I beg your pardon. If I dwell on them, that's because
I am the Emperor. . . ."

54   "Ah, what a pity!"

"And because, being a great wise man, you may be chosen one day to take up the burden of the Empire."

"By no means, by no means. That would insult me."

With this retort Shu-yu was moved by a nervous reaction and rose in spite of himself. But, trying to restrain his indignation, he sat down again at once, and the Emperor continued with a quiet and paternal solemnity:

"I beg you. I now address the great wise man, the most capable subject of the Empire. I'll die serenely if he agrees to be my successor as Emperor."

"Indeed, your honest confidence overpowers me. But you forget my flowers, my stars, my walks about hills and waters, in short, my freedom. Besides, and don't take offense at this, I always believe that spring water is clear in the mountains but impure once it has left them. Please, let me hear no more of this . . . unwonted proposal."

"What can I do to make you consent?"

"Don't trouble about that and I'll be very grateful to you."

"Can nothing be done?"

"Nothing."

They remained silent a while. The Emperor was regretful, but still admired Shu-yu and respected his feelings. Far from being flattered, the wise man appeared annoyed. At last the Emperor took his leave, saying:

"I am more sorry than I can say; naturally, not for you but for the Empire, for myself."

The next morning Shu-yu went early up to the spring to wash his ears. No sooner had he begun than old-man Father 55 of Nests came with his cow to drink. He saluted the well-known wise man at once:

"I hope I find you well, venerable Shu-yu."

"Thank you; and you also, venerable Father of Nests."

"Now you are washing your face here, aren't you?"

"No, I am washing only my ears."

"Your ears? What for?"

"Because they were soiled by something . . . sullying."

Continuing his ablutions, Shu-yu related the visit of the Emperor and what had ensued. Father of Nests concluded:

"On the whole, that's your fault."

"My fault? I never asked him to come that I know of."

"That's all the same."

"You are out of your mind."

"Not at all. I'll explain to you. Why did he come? Because he valued you. Why did he value you? Because your wisdom is an object of universal admiration. Why is that so? Because you sought it. After all, it never comes of itself. Never!"

Then Shu-yu washed his face as well, for it had become very red. As for Father of Nests, he took his cow upstream, murmuring:

"Come, Snaffi, we'll go and drink farther up; here the water is dirtied by this gentleman's ear washing."

All this, fortunately, did not hinder the Emperor Yao from finding a worthy successor. Shwang, the other wise man, accepted. And, following the footsteps of the Emperor Yao, he insured the peace, happiness, and prosperity of the whole nation. So their two reigns are known as the Golden Age of

56 Chinese history.

The Reward

In ancient times in China, there were many private schools. They were situated generally in Buddhist temples and run by a schoolmaster. The schoolmaster was usually a man who had failed to pass his examinations and was paid by his pupils at a rather low rate.

The one in this story lived with his old mother in a humble house behind a temple where he had his school. Though thirty-five, he had not yet married because of his poverty.

One day a gentleman, a former Chancellor of the Empire, came back in retirement to the town with a brilliant retinue and many riches. It was repeatedly suggested to the schoolmaster that he ask help from this rich man, so as to enlarge his school and make it thrive. But his integrity and pride prevented him from doing so, because the former dignitary was said to have done many a wrong thing in the Capital in order to become rich.

On the other hand, the schoolmaster and his mother often shared the little they had with two unknown women—a pretty girl and her mother—who had come mysteriously and installed themselves in the temple, as was the custom of the homeless. The mother, old and feeble, almost a bedridden invalid, was tenderly cared for by her energetic daughter. They lived on the offerings that the girl gathered in different parts of town from her performances of sword juggling and leaping. When the performances were over or the weather was bad, she would practice in the corridors of the temple to improve her skill. These were delightful moments for the schoolmaster, who could then admire her at close quarters. He had fallen in love with her. She? Nobody could tell. Though she sometimes smiled at him, she always appeared too busy to notice his love.

Finally after long deliberation with his mother, the schoolmaster summoned up the courage to ask for her hand. She refused. Some months later he renewed his request. She refused again.

Meanwhile, she became happier and happier as her skill improved, and one night she came by herself to the young man. Overjoyed, puzzled, and somewhat shy, he did not really know what to do. Then she said with a frank smile:

"You desire me, you want me, you love me. Here I am. Take me. Forget your scruples and ideas of Rite."

Recovering from his astonishment, he could not but give himself up to her argument, and they had a delicious night.

The next night he went to her "to ask for joy." The door was closed. In vain he knocked. He waited till the dawn. During the day he looked forward to an explanation, but she went on as usual, smiling, juggling, and leaping, but did not answer to his questions.

He bore this awkward situation for thirty days. On the

thirty-first night she came once more by herself and they passed another night together.

One night two months later he went to try to ask her for joy. But what was his surprise to see through the window that the girl and her mother were making sacrifice in front of the tablet of her father with the head of the rich dignitary and candles and incense; she was saying piously:

"Father, I have avenged you. Just now I leapt into the residence of the man who ordered your death, so unjustly and for money, and with my sword I cut off his head."

Far from the joy he wanted to ask for, the schoolmaster returned home overpowered.

As he knew her character, the next day he did not ask for any explanation, and she behaved as though nothing had happened, except that she seemed more serene and more a woman.

Seven months later she came one morning with a newborn boy and gave it to the schoolmaster's mother, saying:

"This is the reward I wanted to give to you. You are too poor to give your son in marriage. You would thus have no offspring and it would be a terrible injustice; people so good and so upright deserve a descendant. Besides, though so poor yourself, you have always been helpful to us, strangers to you. To reward your virtue and to express my gratitude I give you the best gift you could ever dream of. Take care of him, bring him up well, inculcate your virtues on him. We are leaving tomorrow morning. Do not worry about us or look for us."

After their departure no more was heard of them.

Fetal Education

Once upon a time there was a man who saw no-body but himself, paid attention to nobody but himself, and cared for nobody but himself. And in his bearing he was maliciously impolite. So he was known as the "impolite man."

In spite of the adage "Two different persons never sleep in the same bed," the wife of the "impolite man" was quite different from him. He was pretentious, cynical, proud, and rough, whereas she was candid, delicate, modest, and dainty. Yet, imbued with ancient principles—especially the one recommending women "to finish their lives with a sole man"—the poor creature had no recourse but to bear him with patience and resignation.

Not only did he render their home a living hell, but he took unpleasantness, annoyances, and quarrels wherever he went. The following instance shows clearly his character.

In contrast to his household, that of his wife's sister was perfect. She had the most accomplished husband alive. The couple were quite young, well to do, and suited to each other, even in their superstitions. Their only problem was the absence of children. They had had three children, but all three had died at an early age. They wondered constantly and with bitterness at the death of their offspring. The children were robust in constitution and perfectly cared for and nursed. Why did they die one after another?

At last they found out the cause. It must lie, they thought, in the ill-omened words their brother-in-law, the "impolite man," uttered in abundance at the hundredth day feast of each child. To be sure, it did.

They were very happy at this discovery, for the next time they could take precautions. Unfortunately the next time did not come. Since they respected the Confucian precept that runs, "One of the three disgraces of filial piety is to have no offspring," they were awfully worried at this. They did everything possible to remedy it. Each time they were going to display "clouds and rain," they offered incense to the tablets of their ancestors, murmuring the aforesaid precept. They even made vows to Kwang Ying, the Goddess of Mercy, that she might grant them a child again. To please Her, the wife followed a vegetable diet on certain days of each month. And, on meat days, she ate all sorts of peculiar things which, according to popular belief, favor conception, such as bamboo saplings, roots of bananas, and chickens with black feet and black bones.

Whether it was because of all this or not, she was at length with child again. The preparations for the birth and feasts were, needless to say, minutely arranged. Well in advance, they prayed, threatened, and implored by turns their brother-in-law to spare them his words of ill omen this time. 63

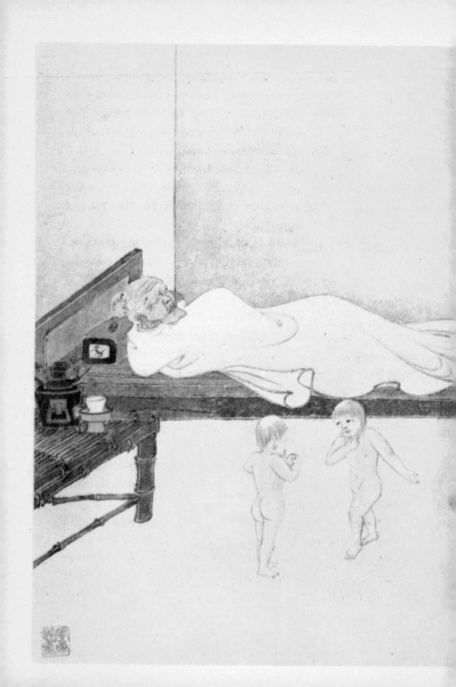

By a strange chance, the "impolite man" was not as sarcastic as usual, because his wife, too, had conceived. The prospect of becoming a father had apparently lessened his impoliteness. His wife was perplexed. On the one hand, she was naturally pleased to have a child, but on the other hand, she was terrified at the thought of hereditary defect.

Meanwhile, the superstitious couple had their child. The feasts of the third day and the first month passed well; that meant that the "impolite man," a relative who had had to be invited, had said nothing wrong on those two occasions. Yet they were worried about the hundredth day feast, the most important. But, in fact, on that day all were amazed at the absence of venemous darts from the "impolite man." Naturally he had spoken, in fact spoken at length, but he did not say anything which forebode evil. The day before, his wife had pleaded with him for a long time.

The ceremony was over; all had gone well. The guests took their leave. No longer able to contain himself, or wanting the malicious pleasure of taking revenge without actual cause, the "impolite man" turned at the doorway and said:

"I have said nothing of ill omen this time, huh! If this child dies like the others, it won't be my fault."

After this scene at which they could neither laugh nor weep, the wife of the "impolite man" was more preoccupied than ever about her coming child. She had great faith in the theory of heredity. So she went, unknown to her husband, to consult doctors. They were unable to help her. However, the one with whom she pleaded most showed her a way. He said:

"In the present state of science, we can do almost nothing about this. But, if you like, you may try the fetal hypnotic method."

"It's a new method, isn't it?"

"Oh, yes, very new."

"Is it efficacious?"

"I hope so."

"Of what does this method consist?

"It consists of prenatal education."

"That'll be fine. Describe it to me quickly, please."

"As its name indicates, this prenatal education has as its object the formation of children's characters before they come into the world, according to the wishes of the children's parents."

"How learned you are."

"In your case, what is the essential point to inculcate upon the coming child? Politeness?"

"Yes, yes, politeness!"

"Well, you can inculcate this quality on him by telling him to be polite as often as possible. By dint of always hearing the same thing, his brain in formation will absorb it, which will produce the required effect."

"How wonderful! But what procedure must I follow?"

"To simplify things, repeat three times the sentence 'Be polite, my child,' looking at your abdomen, on getting up and on going to sleep."

"So, six times a day."

"Exactly. But you must say this formula with tenderness and conviction as if you were uttering a spell."

67

"I'll do all this and I hope, in about six months, I shall come and thank you with my very polite child."

"Good luck, Madam!"

She carried out the doctor's instructions very faithfully since they were the only instructions she had received. Her love for her future child made her anxious to be doubly sure, so she repeated the formula not only at the prescribed times but whenever an opportunity presented itself, in the bath for instance. Naturally, in so doing, she had to withstand the mockery, taunts, and anger of her husband who swore the child would be an authentic idiot.

Things went normally, except that she was more than ordinarily big. Soon, the time of the birth arrived. Everything was ready, but nothing happened. The nine months had passed. Ten months, one year, still nothing. Doctors were summoned but they could do nothing. Years passed, five, ten, twenty. By this time the abnormality had become almost normal.

At length at the age of eighty, the overly devoted mother died. Her body was immediately taken by the Medical Society and, for scientific purposes, opened. What was the doctor's surprise to find in the womb two little men with long white beards, who were murmuring politely to each other:

"After you, pray!"

"No, I beg you, after you."

"Not at all!"

"Please, please!"

Tso Ying Tie

Once upon a time, in the 4th century, there was a couple who were ideally happy but for one thing —they had no heir. They had a thriving business in tea and a neat household, and they loved each other fondly. They had been married for ten years, but Heaven had not yet granted them a son.

At last the wife conceived. Overjoyed, they prayed and prayed to all the gods and goddesses that a male child be given them. According to the customs of the time, a female could not become an heir. Unfortunately their hopes were dashed. The newborn child belonged to Eve's sex.

According to a popular belief a girl dressed as a boy from birth was supposed to "attract brothers." The couple put this belief into practice and even gave her a boy's name— Ying Tie.

For business reasons the family Tso, that being their name, moved from Shang Yu to a neighboring town, Whai Kee. There the child was a boy to all extent and purposes and she studied with other boys for several years. A boy named Liang Shan Peh became her inseparable friend.

They were of the same age and had the same tastes and character; their "hearts reflected each other." During recreation time they played together; on holidays they made excursions together. Their mutual affection increased as time passed. At the age of fifteen, their parents permitted them to go to visit the boy's aunt at Heaven Eye Mountain. There they had two months of perfect and innocent bliss.

They would get up with the rising of the sun and take long walks through the green hills which were abundant in that region. Often they would picnic under the shade of a large tree, and after eating they would rest side by side. Their perfect and pure bodies were in harmony with the blue sky, the opening flower buds, and the tranquil murmur of streams. They were part of nature.

Once the boy suggested they go to a far and deep stream for a swim. She seemed reluctant. Since he insisted, they finally went. As soon as they arrived he dived into the water, but she remained on the bank, somewhat awkwardly. A voice from the water soon aroused her:

"Come along. What are you waiting for?"

"No, I'll stay here."

"Why?"

"I don't like the water."

"What nonsense; it's such fun."

"Go on and enjoy yourself. I'll look after the lunch basket."

"Silly boy! You don't know what you're missing by not swimming."

70   As usual they had their lunch under the trees, quite gaily

and with good appetite. Afterward, while resting side by side, she asked:

"Are you angry with me?"

"Why should I be?"

"Because I didn't join you in the water."

"Nonsense! It's just a question of what a person likes. Anyway, you're the loser."

"We are so happy here."

"Yes, perfectly happy."

"I should love to rest like this always . . . always with you."

"I should, too."

After some moments of silence, he went on:

"What a pity one of us is not a girl."

"We should be an ideal couple."

"Of course. That's what I thought."

"Let's swear then."

"Swear what?"

"That if ever in the present life we cannot be united as husband and wife, we shall be so in the next."

"What nonsense!"

"Why, won't you swear that?"

"Yes, I will, but, I mean, why did you say 'if ever'?"

"I don't know why."

"Well, let's swear. Let's do it properly. Stand up, will you?"

Then, the two very solemnly made their oaths. And about twilight they went home, with some rare clouds moving in the sky and occasional birds flying to their nests.

With the fall of the leaves, their holidays ended. Back in town they continued to see each other every day. But soon they were obliged to separate. Her parents decided to return to their native town. The separation was especially painful since they did not know whether they would see or hear from each other again (considering the difficulty of communication in those days).

On the way home the parents dressed Ying Tie as a girl. She was so beautiful that they were dumbfounded. After they had settled down once more in their native town, they began to think of the marriage of their beloved daughter. She, however, always whispered, "I am still too young; we have time."

But time passed quickly. Two years had come and gone since their return. In vain the parents chose young men one after another for their daughter with every care; not one of them was accepted by her.

One day they suggested an exceptionally deserving suitor; she refused obstinately. Her parents finally became impatient, especially the father, who remonstrated with her for the first time in his life. The girl did not reply; she only wept. The mother did not know what to do. There was a real problem in the family. At length the girl vowed to her mother that she would only marry her childhood friend. When they saw how decided she was in this, the parents made inquiries about the boy.

After a long and difficult search, they were told that he had become ill some months earlier and died. They hoped that
74 she would forget in time and so broke the news gently to

her. Day and night she asked to visit his tomb; promising that when she had performed this pious duty, she could then consider marriage.

So the three undertook the journey. When they arrived, though the girl was exhausted she went at once to the grave, where, kneeling, she wept. Suddenly, through her tears, she saw the tomb open by itself and the boy come out. They kissed, they kissed. . . . And she fell . . . dead.

They buried her beside him.

The above story is recorded in the local records of Whai Kee, in the province of Chekiang.

Gratitude

Once upon a time a peasant was coming back from the town where he went to give some produce of his farm as a present to a hospital.

Every time he had the opportunity to do a good deed, he felt contented, joyful, and at peace with himself. So this day he was humming a tune while passing through a large forest on the way back.

At a crossing a fox came to him. It was panting, exhausted, and shivering with fear. It begged him:

"Help, help, save me! I'm being chased by a cruel hunter."

(*a muttering sound*)

"Please, a life is in danger."

"I'm willing to save you, but how can I do it?"

"You can hide me in your basket and not say anything about me to the hunter if he questions you."

"Well, get in the basket quickly."

The peasant lifted the top of the basket and the fox jumped in. And he went on.

Having walked just a few steps, he was called by a hunter coming from a side path:

"Look here, my good fellow, a fox should have passed through here. Which way has it gone?"

"Well, well, a fox. No, I haven't seen any."

"Oh damn that fox. I'll have to find it again."

Convinced that the fox had gone straight on, the hunter rushed after it.

After having been so scared, the fox whispered in the basket:

"What a saint this man is. I owe him everlasting gratitude. This action of his deserves a reward."

After walking a mile, the peasant, thinking the danger over for the fox, opened the basket and the fox jumped out. He shook himself, stretched, and smoothed his fur. Since all these emotions made him hungry, the fox said to the peasant:

"I'm hungry."

"Poor thing, unfortunately I have no food on me."

"Are you sure?"

"Positive. You can see yourself."

"I see quite well; there's something on you good to eat."

"What?"

"Your flesh."

"What flesh? My flesh?"

"Yes, the flesh on your cheeks, the flesh on your chest. Well, the flesh on you."

The peasant was stunned and a shiver of fear ran through his body. He stammered:

"How can you think of such a thing? I just saved your life and now you want to take mine. Is that the way you show your gratitude? You're only an animal after all."

77

"Gratitude, gratitude, that word doesn't mean as much to us as it does to men."

The fox started petting the peasant's neck. Trying to find a way to escape, the peasant said:

"Wait a moment. Justice does not allow . . ."

(again a word without meaning)

"True, these notions have no grip on you. Arguing with you is just a waste of time. We'd better go and ask the advice of others."

"What others?"

"Other men."

"They belong to your kind and will support you. Though only an animal, I'll grant you a few hours delay. We'll go to ask advice of a tree, an animal, and a human being. I'm certain they will find me right, because, you see, I'm always good. Men would never agree to giving such a delay, because they believe that 'a bird in the hand is worth two in the bush.' "

At the edge of the forest they asked an old, gnarled, branchless apple tree. The apple tree answered:

"Actually, gratitude and justice have never existed, except on the lips of men or in their writings. I am myself a wonderful example of this. As long as I bore fruit, they pruned me, watered me, and gave fertilizers to my roots. Now that I am barren they let me die. If you can, old boy, eat this man; so we can all get revenge for man's ingratitude."

Farther on, they asked a gaunt, lean-ribbed cow, which held the same view as the fox. Then, thinking aloud, the cow

78 said:

"I don't see why this fox should not enjoy its rescuer's flesh, since men have the saying "every man for himself," and their lives are led in selfishness. I have had myself a very sad experience. When I was fat, the farmers fed me well, and when ill, they took care of me as if I were their own daughter. Now that I have no more milk, you can't imagine the treatment I receive."

Finally, they asked an old man. They told him the whole story. He listened carefully to what was being said to him, thought it over, and, scratching his head, announced formally:

"Oh, there is no doubt about this case. I approve the way of thinking of the apple tree and the cow. But I think there is something not quite clear in this matter. I wonder how you, with your bulky fur, could ever hide in such a small basket?"

Overcome with pride, the fox cried:

"It's nothing. I'll show you right now."

And he jumped into the basket. At this very moment, glancing cunningly at the peasant, the old man shouted:

"Hurry up, shut the basket, you fool!"

Illusion

One day Tswang Tze, the Taoist philosopher-magician, went to see a friend with his disciple, whom Yorkshiremen would call almost "a natural"; that is, a person lacking normal intelligence. On the way they loitered about a pond and gazed at the fish in it. Suddenly the master cried:

"How happy they are!"

Doubtful, the disciple said:

"You are not a fish, so how do you know they are happy?"

"You are not me, so how do you know that I don't know they are happy?"

The disciple, having no reply and wishing to change the subject, then said:

"Pray, come. We'll be late. We have still to find good wood in the forest."

They started again and entered the forest. Some distance farther on, there was a tree so big that it would take six men to encircle it. But the philosopher went on as though he had not seen it. Surprised, the natural inquired:

"Master, there is a very big tree. Why do you not stop to examine it?"

"It's useless."

"Why?"

"Because its wood is surely bad; otherwise it would not have been left to grow so big. Do you remember my words: The best things are always taken first?"

At length, they arrived at the friend's house where they were received with open arms. To entertain the visitors, the friend ordered his servant to kill a goose. The latter asked which of the two geese he was to kill. His master responded that the one which quacked less well was to be killed. This choice confounded the disciple, who could not help exclaiming:

"Master, you have just said that the best things are always taken first; now this gentleman has kept the better of the geese. How do you explain that?"

"There's nothing to explain; its as plain as good morning. If there were fixed rules governing things here below, our life would be worthless. Conditions, circumstances, contingencies . . ."

"Stop, please. Let me digest your last teaching."

The lunch went well, and the visitors took their leave very cordially. To enjoy the landscape, they went home by a different route. Halfway, they saw a pretty young woman in mourning, quietly and incessantly fanning a recently built tomb. Intrigued, the philosopher sent his disciple to make inquiries. But the woman disdained to reply. He then approached her himself. Bowing very courteously, he said: 83

"Honorable lady, my respects. I apologize if I disturb you. As a philosopher, may I ask why you fan this recently built tomb?"

The lady paused a while, hesitated, closed her large and beautiful fan and, at length, replied in a whisper:

"Because of my great misfortune."

"I grieve to hear it. But I don't see the connection . . ."

"It's difficult to understand, I agree."

"May I ask for an explanation?"

With a sigh, the lady explained:

"My late husband and I loved each other deeply. His health was precarious. In order to prove his profound comprehension, his unselfishness, and, I'll say, his uncommon love, he always recommended that I marry again immediately after his death. With anxiety and insistence, he repeated this wish on his death bed. I was—and I am still—grief stricken. Distracted, I had nothing to calm his anxiety but the promise to do so, with, however, the reserve that I wait till his tomb dried. He then imposed the condition that I dry it conscientiously with a large fan, and made me swear to it. I swore. Now I am keeping my oath."

"You are admirable. Please permit me to help you."

"I don't know if I may accept your kindness."

"Do, pray, give me your fan. I'll dry the grave."

The lady did as he asked. The philosopher fanned with vigor for five minutes or so. The whole tomb became dry almost instantly. Bewildered and amazed but grateful, the lady offered the fan to him as a remembrance. She

lingered a little by the grave and went away slowly, pensively. So he also went home with his always puzzled disciple, in the opposite direction.

*　　*　　*

Mrs. Tswang Tze, though middle aged, was still attractive with her liquid eyes, sensual mouth, and shapely breasts. Waiting for her husband that afternoon she began to feel lonely and to miss him. So much so that when he returned, she said poutingly:

"Why are you so late?"

The disciple hastened to reply with great glee:

"We have had a lot of adventures. Listen . . ."

The master interrupted him reproachfully:

"He who hastens to answer, though not addressed, shows signs of egoism."

When the talkative fellow had retired at that hint, Mrs. Tswang inquired again:

"Are you tired? . . . Oh, what a beautiful fan! Who gave it to you? It's a lady's."

He then detailed the whole adventure while she broke in several times with disapproval and indignation. Nevertheless, he concluded:

"I maintain that that woman was admirable."

"As usual, you like paradoxes."

"No, no, it's not so. I must add that her late husband was admirable, too. He knew perfectly well the truth I used to tell you: 'Nature sometimes speaks louder than learned virtue.' "

87

"All the same, she was not faithful."

"Do you think you'd be more so?"

"What! How could you ask such a thing? You ought to know me better than that. . . ."

So saying, she grew hysterical. He had difficulty in calming her down.

After this storm in a teacup, the couple went on living happily with the disciple whose naturalness pleased them very much as a distraction. Unfortunately the master was suddenly taken ill one day and died after a few hours. His wife was overcome with grief. But the disciple showed little feeling, thinking that such a great spirit could not die like that.

Both were very busy, laying out the body, preparing for the funeral, dealing with undertakers, and replying to condolences. Since the philosopher had no children, the disciple acted in place of his son. The poor fellow was nearly driven mad with the news that the wife wanted to commit suicide. To check her, he urged:

"With one dead, we two have already too much to do. If you die now, I'll be left alone with two dead. What would I do? Have pity on me, please, please . . ."

Had the wife not been so deep in grief, she would have laughed at his childish but truthful argument. However, she abandoned her lugubrious idea.

The third day after the death, a princely disciple arrived from a neighboring state. He prostrated himself three times before the coffin while the wife and the natural did likewise, as politeness required. In doing so, the wife perceived, through her tears, the limpid eyes, expressive eyebrows, and powderlike skin of the newcomer.

When the ceremony was over, the prince begged that he might greet the mistress. He then asked her permission to remain for the burial (generally, Chinese don't bury the deceased before seven sevens, that is 49 days) and to collect and arrange the notes, thoughts, and manuscripts of the master. This she granted, and he was installed in the house.

Far from having a pretentious manner, the prince behaved very simply and, thereby, gained the sympathy of all. Only the wife felt uneasy and awkward in his presence. Each time she saw him, the thought of her first impression of him made her blush a little and lower her eyes. But when he was not present, she had a vague desire to see him, so much did his image occupy her mind.

As for the natural, he was delighted with his co-disciple, who showed himself extremely friendly to him, while the prince's servant helped in all he had to do, and he had indeed much to do. Therefore, all were more or less happy, if one could speak of happiness in a house of death.

This state of things did not last. The prince fell seriously ill. His old servant was beside himself with anxiety and sorrow. Both the wife and the disciple went to see the sick man whose headache was so terrible that he could not utter a word and scarcely recognized them. The disciple was, this time, rather worried. He sat motionless at the bedside of the prince. The wife then went out with the old servant to discuss the nature and eventual cure of his master's illness. Sobbing, the old servant said:

"It is a chronic illness. But this time there is no hope."

"Why?"

"Alas, Madam, nothing can be done."

"But we must do everything possible."

"In our own state, it would be easy."

"Why?"

"We have so many men condemned to death and, if need be, we can always procure somebody."

"What?"

"My master's recovery can only be assured by a human brain."

"A human brain?"

"Yes, Madam."

"The brain of a living man?"

"Yes! But, failing that, the brain of a man recently dead. As you see, there is nothing to be done here. Poor prince, dead so young! He *was* so clever, so handsome, and so indulgent."

"Oh! How can I save him? . . . Now go to your master."

She pondered and pondered again over this. Suddenly, a little ray of light dawned in her brain. It grew bigger and bigger and from it an idea formed.

That very evening she took a hatchet and went straight to her husband's coffin. Once before it, she began to chop with the intention of opening it and then taking his brain. As if by witchery, the coffin yielded under her blows. Soon Tswang Tze appeared, more alive than ever, with a quiet but tender "well." The hatchet fell from her hands, and she fell in a faint. At that moment the disciple came in, crying:

"Mistress, mistress, the prince and his servant have gone, disappeared!"

He saw then the philosopher, sitting on his coffin. Frightened, he recoiled, exclaiming:

"You! Are you yourself or a ghost?"

"I am myself, I presume."

"I said such a great spirit could not die like that. You see, you are not dead. Mistress will be so happy, so happy. She who wanted to commit suicide. I'll go to tell her."

"She's down there."

"Oh, goodness. She has been overwhelmed, no doubt."

"Come, let's take her up and put her on the bed."

So they hoisted the unfortunate wife and removed her to her room. While they were about it, the natural found the leisure to inquire:

"Master, I think all this is only an act to teach me life, isn't it?"